A Million Times Forever

BY SHAWN POST-KLAUBER

ISBN: 978-0-578-88439-4

Cataloging-in-Publication Data is on file at the
Library of Congress:1-10054576421

Book design by TeaBerryCreative.com

Dedication

A Million Times Forever is dedicated to all children who have the desire to learn about and to love nature. Especially, to my grandchildren, who, through the eyes of their adoring grandparents, have added beauty to the garden through their love of nature.

"In nature, nothing is perfect and everything is perfect. Trees can be contorted, bent in weird ways, and they're still beautiful."
—ALICE WALKER

I'd like to express my deepest gratitude to the administration and volunteers at the Fairchild Tropical Botanic Gardens for their dedication and expertise and the use of their website information and several of their beautiful photographs.

There is a happy place that children and adults love to visit. It is a very special place and people go there to enjoy and learn about nature.

What is nature, you ask?

Well, nature is a word that describes the beautiful parts of our earth that man does not make. Nature may be the trees you see on your street or the flowers in front of your house. It may be the grasshoppers you see hiding in the plants or the geese that walk by the pond. It may be the rocks you collect by the river. It may be the butterflies that flutter about the garden.

This is the story of a girl named Celeste and her younger brother, Jaxson. The story is about how this sister and brother learned to love nature.

One sunny but cool day, Celeste's and Jaxson's grandparents took the children for their second visit to Fairchild Tropical Botanic Garden. They had so much fun the first time they visited that they could not wait to visit The Garden again.

The children began their day by walking through the rain forest. There they saw the waterfalls and heard the rush of water all around them. The rainforest was the coolest place in The Garden.

A rainforest is an area of many trees where the weather is very warm and there is lots of rainfall. Celeste and Jaxson had fun following the path through the rain forest and discovering many of the different plants and animals that lived there.

Celeste and Jaxson were very excited to see the butterflies at the Wings of the Tropics Butterfly Conservatory. At any time, you can see hundreds of butterflies of all different colors. It was like looking at a "flying rainbow" over your head. Sometimes, the butterflies would land on the children's hands and clothes. You could even see the butterflies eating their favorite fruits such as apples, oranges, and bananas.

Next stop, the cannonball tree! This was the children's favorite tree in The Garden. The tree is very big and can grow up to 75 feet tall! Its fruit grows right on the trunk.

"It looks like a tree that is covered with spaghetti and has giant meatballs growing all over it," said Jaxson. The children and their grandparents decided that every time they visited the tree, they were going to sing the song, "On Top of Spaghetti!"

Lunch time! What should we have to eat? Since their last trip to The Garden, the children had wanted to go back to the Glasshouse Café to have their favorite lunch...grilled cheese sandwiches with lemonade...and, also, to see the butterflies from the inside of the café.

While they were eating lunch, Celeste asked if they could go to the gift shop. Grandma said that was fine. But first, they were going to see the flower exhibits. Celeste said that she had already seen them on her last visit. Grandma explained, "Celeste, when we see something so beautiful in nature, we can see it a million times forever. That is what the beauty of nature is all about!"

After lunch, it was time to meet Marjorie! The statue of Marjorie Stoneman Douglas sitting on a bench is just outside of the café. In her lifetime, she worked to save the Everglades from being destroyed. She is called a conservationist. To conserve means to save or protect what you love. She helped to conserve nature and she lived to be 108 years old!

Jaxson went up to see her on the bench, rubbed her arm, and said, "Thank you, Marjorie for all of the beautiful plants, and trees, and animals that can now live in The Garden."

Time to play! Next stop, the lawn behind the café. There is lots of room there for picnics and playing catch. Grandpa helped us collect branches and build nests for the birds that fly in The Garden.

"Race you back to the picnic tables, Celeste," says Jaxson.

Grandpa says, "Let's go to see the fish in the pond." Grandpa loves to see fish anywhere! So, they all walked to the pond. The colorful cichlids were swimming all around. If you look carefully, you might even find a koi fish. In Japan, koi fish are thought to bring good luck.

The beautiful sculpture in the middle of the pond was made by a very famous artist named Dale Chihuly. You can find many kinds of artwork all around The Garden.

As the children and their grandparents were walking around The Garden, they saw something very special. "Look over there," said Jaxson. "I think someone is getting married!"

Looking over the stone wall, they saw a bride and a groom who were walking down the aisle. Celeste said, "Grandma, I feel like I am in a dream!" But it was not a dream. It was for real!

It was quite a busy day. The family decided to take the tram back to the gift shop. The children rested as they looked out the sides of the tram. On the way, they saw many other beautiful places in The Garden.

The tram dropped them off at their last stop: the gift shop. Celeste and Jaxson picked out a beautiful flower vase to bring home to their mom and dad. There were also children's toys and beautiful jewelry to look at. It was a fun finish to another happy day.

As they were leaving the gift shop and walking to their car, Celeste told her grandma and grandpa, "I wish that we could go back to The Garden a million times forever!"

A Million Times Forever

Comprehension Questions for Home Discussion, Individualized or Classroom Assignments, or Computerized Reading Programs:

Q1.   Who took Celeste and Jaxson to The Garden?
Ⓐ their teacher Ⓑ their mom and dad Ⓒ their grandparents

Q2.   How many times did the children in the story visit The Garden?
This is their: Ⓐ first time Ⓐ second time Ⓐ third time

Q3.   What does a "conservationist" do?
Ⓐ build bridges Ⓑ fly planes Ⓒ protect nature

Q4.   Which one is not an example of nature?
Ⓐ rain forests Ⓑ library buildings Ⓒ butterfly gardens

Q5. Where did Celeste tell her grandmother that she wanted to go?

Ⓐ the flower garden Ⓑ the tram ride Ⓒ the gift shop

Q6. What did Grandpa like to see the most at the gardens?

Ⓐ the fishpond Ⓑ the butterfly garden Ⓒ the flower show

Q7. What did Celeste and Jaxson buy at the gift shop?

Ⓐ a flower vase Ⓑ a toy lizard Ⓒ a book about animals

Q8. How did the children go back to the gift shop at the end of the day?

Ⓐ by walking Ⓑ by riding a bike Ⓒ by riding the tram

Q9. What was the first name of the lady who was sitting on the bench?

Ⓐ Mary Ⓑ Marjorie Ⓒ Mandy

Q10. In what country are koi fish thought to bring good luck?

Ⓐ England Ⓑ United States Ⓒ Japan

About Fairchild Tropical Botanic Gardens

Fairchild Tropical Botanic Garden is an 83-acre attraction which opened to the public in 1938. It is located in the city of Coral Gables, Florida which is just south of Miami. Fairchild is "a museum, laboratory, learning center and conservation research facility whose main role is preserving biodiversity." In 2012, Fairchild became the home of the American Orchid Society. It boasts 45,000 members and over 1,200 volunteers. You can stroll through the garden on your own or enjoy a free, narrated tour on your visit. Either way, Fairchild Tropical Botanic Garden is truly a trip through a tropical paradise.

Contributing Photographer

In addition to her photography, Jennifer Araneda Post has served as an Assistant Principal for a bilingual public school in Jacksonville, Florida as well as a guidance counselor. She is proud to be the mother of Celeste and Jaxson who were the impetus for this true story.

About the Author

Dr. Shawn Post-Klauber is an associate professor and former associate dean specializing in literacy at the University of Miami School of Education and Human Development. She is also a Licensed School Psychologist.

Dr. Post has been a long-time member of Fairchild Tropical Botanical Garden and serves on the board of The Lucy Project which advocates for children who struggle to read and provides full and fair access to evidence-based literacy intervention.

Dr. Post serves as a Professor-in Residence at Ponce De Leon Middle School and has a private practice in assessment of children for gifted and children and adolescents with learning and educational needs.

CPSIA information can be obtained
at www.ICGtesting.com
Printed in the USA
LVHW072307130521
687425LV00001B/26